I ♥ UNICORNS

Have fun completing the
sticker and colouring activities
in this sweet unicorn book.

Where there is a missing sticker,
you will see an empty shape. Search your
sticker pages to find the missing sticker.

Don't forget about the card pages at the back of
the book! Press out and create your own magical
unicorn models, and decorate a dreamy
door hanger to put on display.

make
believe
ideas

Unicorn Palace

Use stickers and colour
to complete the scene.

Sticker some ducks on the pond.

How many toadstools
can you see?

....

Picture puzzle

Find the missing stickers,
and then circle three purple things.

st_r

wa_d

_rown

Write the missing letters to finish the words.

Star maze

Guide Blueberry the unicorn through the star-shaped maze to reach her friend.

Start

Finish

How many red stars can you count? ......

Colourful coach

Connect the dots to complete the picture, and then colour it in.

Lovely letters

Find the missing stickers.
Then, use the pictures to
unscramble the words below.

o
r   w
c   n

_ _ _ _ _

l
e   e
j
w

_ _ _ _ _

a
c   s
l
t   e

_ _ _ _ _ _

d
w
n   a

_ _ _ _

Fantastic feasts

Amber is cooking up a fantastic feast.

Circle the one that doesn't belong.

Colour the lollipops.

Doodle yummy toppings on the cupcake.

Sticker the lollipops to finish the pattern.

Candyfloss clouds

Stardust is flying through the clouds.
Draw a line from start to finish.

Start →

Visit all the clouds and rainbows along the way.

Avoid the shooting stars!

→ Finish

Radiant rainbows

Colour the rainbows and candyfloss clouds.
Use the coloured dots as a guide.

Sparkly party

Happy is having a party!
Sticker the beautiful bunting.
Use colour and stickers to decorate Happy.

How many fairies can you see? ......

Find the difference

Circle five differences between the two scenes.

Magical maths

Find the missing stickers to help
Stardust the unicorn finish the sums.

$2 + 2 = 4$

$1 + 3 =$

$4 + 2 =$

$3 + 4 =$

Waterfall wander

Follow the lines to see which unicorn is going to the waterfall.

Pretty patterns

Colour and sticker to complete the pattern.

Unicorn quiz

Look at the rows of unicorns and find the ones that are different.

Who has a crown?	Who has a purple jewel on their ear?	Who wears an orange bow?	Who has gold hooves?

Sticker the correct number in the circles.

1 2 3 4

5 6 7 8

Sparkle stars

Trace the dots to create patterns in the night sky.

Sticker some sparkly stars.

Use colour to complete the scene.

Magic models

Make your very own fairy-tale unicorns! Press out the shapes and shade the reverse sides. Then, prop up the pieces using the stands.

Dreamy door hanger

Press out the hanger, and then decorate it with your stickers.

This room belongs to

....

Page 2

Page 3

Page 4

Page 5

Page 6

Page 7

Page 9

Page 10

Page 12

Page 13

4

6

7

Page 14

Page 15

Page 16

2 5 6 3